MY PROPHETIC

Dream Journal

The Ultimate Guide to Unlocking Your Dreams

This Journal is a Gift:

To: ....

From: ....

Date: ....

D1293732

Join our School of Dreams at:
www.schooloffreshoil.org

For enquiries, email us at:
info@schooloffreshoil.org

Published by Restoration Publishing

Unlocking your Dreams

Dreams are part of the prophetic communications from the realm of the spirit. There are many records of how God used dreams to speak to people in the bible. There are 21 dreams recorded in the bible. Every dream has a spiritual meaning that requires interpretation. Many people are often prompted about things that will happen in their lives by dreams before they happen but do nothing about it for lack of understanding. Lack of knowledge with interpretation of dreams is a big problem of many Christians. A dream could be bad or good with the power to come to pass, so you must have an idea of what to do with every dream.

Most believers wish they could remember their dreams to use the information to their benefit. The Prophetic Dream Journal is purposely crafted for Christians to direct the user to an effective action plan that brings out the best of every dream. It is your personal journal for dream analysis and interpretation. The process of logging and tracking your dreams in the order listed in this journal will lead you to clues towards understanding your dreams to know what next to do. The journal is a guide to unlocking your dreams to discern if it is a divine message from God or demonic attack. If you don't want to forget your dreams, this is what you need. There are essential pieces of information required when writing down your dreams:

- Date, Time, and Venue
- Your dream description
- Type of dream
- The dominant emotions of the dream
- Emotional scale rating of the dream
- Possible meaning of the dream
- Prayer and scripture response

Whether you always dream or occasionally, Prophetic Dream Journal is a good way to log and remember your dreams. The journal is a treasure that will help all seekers to better understand their emotions and thoughts. This journal can guide you to basic understanding of your dreams. It is easy, simple, and quick to use in recording your spiritual and prophetic dreams.

This journal will make a great gift for any occasion, including birthdays, Christmas, Easter and all anniversaries.

My Prophetic Dream Journal

Date, Time & Venue

Dream Title

Dream Description

_____

_____

_____

_____

_____

_____

_____

_____

_____

_____

Type of Dream: ☐ Warning ☐ Guidance ☐ Bad Dream ☐ Good Dream ☐ Prophetic Dream

What Was the Dominant Emotion(s)?

Positive Emotion	Negative Emotion	Emotion Scale Ratings
☐ Joy	☐ Crying	😃 6 Very Happy
☐ Inspiration	☐ Anxiety	🙂 5
☐ Peace	☐ Panic	😐 4
☐ Happy	☐ Sad	🙁 3
☐ Celebration	☐ Confused	☹ 2
☐ Hope	☐ Grieved	😞 1 Not at a all
☐ Blessed	☐ Traumatise	
☐ Grateful	☐ Worried	

My Prophetic Dream Journal

Explain The Feeling

Possible Meaning of Dream

Prayer and Scripture Response

My Prophetic Dream Journal

Date, Time & Venue

Dream Title

Dream Description

_____
_____
_____
_____
_____
_____
_____
_____
_____
_____

Type of Dream: ☐ Warning ☐ Guidance ☐ Bad Dream ☐ Good Dream ☐ Prophetic Dream

What Was the Dominant Emotion(s)?

Positive Emotion	Negative Emotion	Emotion Scale Ratings
☐ Joy	☐ Crying	😃 6 Very Happy
☐ Inspiration	☐ Anxiety	🙂 5
☐ Peace	☐ Panic	😐 4
☐ Happy	☐ Sad	🙁 3
☐ Celebration	☐ Confused	😟 2
☐ Hope	☐ Grieved	😣 1 Not at a all
☐ Blessed	☐ Traumatise	
☐ Grateful	☐ Worried	

My Prophetic Dream Journal

Explain The Feeling

Possible Meaning of Dream

Prayer and Scripture Response

My Prophetic Dream Journal

Date, Time & Venue

Dream Title

Dream Description

_____
_____
_____
_____
_____
_____
_____
_____
_____
_____

Type of Dream: ☐ Warning ☐ Guidance ☐ Bad Dream ☐ Good Dream ☐ Prophetic Dream

What Was the Dominant Emotion(s)?

Positive Emotion	Negative Emotion	Emotion Scale Ratings
☐ Joy	☐ Crying	6 Very Happy
☐ Inspiration	☐ Anxiety	5
☐ Peace	☐ Panic	4
☐ Happy	☐ Sad	3
☐ Celebration	☐ Confused	2
☐ Hope	☐ Grieved	1 Not at a all
☐ Blessed	☐ Traumatise	
☐ Grateful	☐ Worried	

My Prophetic Dream Journal

Explain The Feeling

Possible Meaning of Dream

Prayer and Scripture Response

My Prophetic Dream Journal

Date, Time & Venue

Dream Title

Dream Description

_____
_____
_____
_____
_____
_____
_____
_____
_____
_____

Type of Dream: ☐ Warning ☐ Guidance ☐ Bad Dream ☐ Good Dream ☐ Prophetic Dream

What Was the Dominant Emotion(s)?

Positive Emotion	Negative Emotion	Emotion Scale Ratings
☐ Joy	☐ Crying	😀 6 Very Happy
☐ Inspiration	☐ Anxiety	🙂 5
☐ Peace	☐ Panic	😐 4
☐ Happy	☐ Sad	🙁 3
☐ Celebration	☐ Confused	😟 2
☐ Hope	☐ Grieved	😞 1 Not at a all
☐ Blessed	☐ Traumatise	
☐ Grateful	☐ Worried	

My Prophetic Dream Journal

Explain The Feeling

Possible Meaning of Dream

Prayer and Scripture Response

My Prophetic Dream Journal

Date, Time & Venue

Dream Title

Dream Description

_____
_____
_____
_____
_____
_____
_____
_____
_____
_____

Type of Dream: ☐ Warning ☐ Guidance ☐ Bad Dream ☐ Good Dream ☐ Prophetic Dream

What Was the Dominant Emotion(s)?

Positive Emotion	Negative Emotion	Emotion Scale Ratings
☐ Joy	☐ Crying	😃 6 Very Happy
☐ Inspiration	☐ Anxiety	🙂 5
☐ Peace	☐ Panic	😐 4
☐ Happy	☐ Sad	🙁 3
☐ Celebration	☐ Confused	😟 2
☐ Hope	☐ Grieved	
☐ Blessed	☐ Traumatise	😞 1 Not at a all
☐ Grateful	☐ Worried	

My Prophetic Dream Journal

Explain The Feeling

Possible Meaning of Dream

Prayer and Scripture Response

My Prophetic Dream Journal

Date, Time & Venue

Dream Title

Dream Description

_____

_____

_____

_____

_____

_____

_____

_____

_____

_____

Type of Dream: ☐ Warning ☐ Guidance ☐ Bad Dream ☐ Good Dream ☐ Prophetic Dream

What Was the Dominant Emotion(s)?

Positive Emotion	Negative Emotion	Emotion Scale Ratings
☐ Joy	☐ Crying	🙂 6 — Very Happy
☐ Inspiration	☐ Anxiety	🙂 5
☐ Peace	☐ Panic	😐 4
☐ Happy	☐ Sad	🙁 3
☐ Celebration	☐ Confused	🙁 2
☐ Hope	☐ Grieved	
☐ Blessed	☐ Traumatise	😞 1 — Not at a all
☐ Grateful	☐ Worried	

My Prophetic Dream Journal

Explain The Feeling

Possible Meaning of Dream

Prayer and Scripture Response

My Prophetic Dream Journal

Date, Time & Venue

Dream Title

Dream Description

_____
_____
_____
_____
_____
_____
_____
_____
_____

Type of Dream: ☐ Warning ☐ Guidance ☐ Bad Dream ☐ Good Dream ☐ Prophetic Dream

What Was the Dominant Emotion(s)?

Positive Emotion	Negative Emotion	Emotion Scale Ratings
☐ Joy	☐ Crying	😀 6 Very Happy
☐ Inspiration	☐ Anxiety	🙂 5
☐ Peace	☐ Panic	😐 4
☐ Happy	☐ Sad	🙁 3
☐ Celebration	☐ Confused	😟 2
☐ Hope	☐ Grieved	😞 1 Not at a all
☐ Blessed	☐ Traumatise	
☐ Grateful	☐ Worried	

My Prophetic Dream Journal

Explain The Feeling

Possible Meaning of Dream

Prayer and Scripture Response

My Prophetic Dream Journal

Date, Time & Venue

Dream Title

Dream Description

_____
_____
_____
_____
_____
_____
_____
_____
_____
_____

Type of Dream: ☐ Warning ☐ Guidance ☐ Bad Dream ☐ Good Dream ☐ Prophetic Dream

What Was the Dominant Emotion(s)?

Positive Emotion	Negative Emotion	Emotion Scale Ratings
☐ Joy	☐ Crying	🙂 6 Very Happy
☐ Inspiration	☐ Anxiety	🙂 5
☐ Peace	☐ Panic	😐 4
☐ Happy	☐ Sad	🙁 3
☐ Celebration	☐ Confused	🙁 2
☐ Hope	☐ Grieved	😞 1 Not at a all
☐ Blessed	☐ Traumatise	
☐ Grateful	☐ Worried	

My Prophetic Dream Journal

Explain The Feeling

Possible Meaning of Dream

Prayer and Scripture Response

My Prophetic Dream Journal

Date, Time & Venue

Dream Title

Dream Description

Type of Dream: ☐ Warning ☐ Guidance ☐ Bad Dream ☐ Good Dream ☐ Prophetic Dream

What Was the Dominant Emotion(s)?

Positive Emotion	Negative Emotion	Emotion Scale Ratings
☐ Joy	☐ Crying	😃 6 Very Happy
☐ Inspiration	☐ Anxiety	🙂 5
☐ Peace	☐ Panic	😐 4
☐ Happy	☐ Sad	🙁 3
☐ Celebration	☐ Confused	
☐ Hope	☐ Grieved	😞 2
☐ Blessed	☐ Traumatise	
☐ Grateful	☐ Worried	😫 1 Not at a all

My Prophetic Dream Journal

Explain The Feeling

Possible Meaning of Dream

Prayer and Scripture Response

My Prophetic Dream Journal

Date, Time & Venue

Dream Title

Dream Description

_____
_____
_____
_____
_____
_____
_____
_____
_____

Type of Dream: ☐ Warning ☐ Guidance ☐ Bad Dream ☐ Good Dream ☐ Prophetic Dream

What Was the Dominant Emotion(s)?

Positive Emotion	Negative Emotion	Emotion Scale Ratings
☐ Joy	☐ Crying	😀 6 — Very Happy
☐ Inspiration	☐ Anxiety	🙂 5
☐ Peace	☐ Panic	😐 4
☐ Happy	☐ Sad	🙁 3
☐ Celebration	☐ Confused	😞 2
☐ Hope	☐ Grieved	😢 1 — Not at all
☐ Blessed	☐ Traumatise	
☐ Grateful	☐ Worried	

My Prophetic Dream Journal

Explain The Feeling

Possible Meaning of Dream

Prayer and Scripture Response

My Prophetic Dream Journal

Date, Time & Venue

Dream Title

Dream Description

_____
_____
_____
_____
_____
_____
_____
_____
_____
_____

Type of Dream: ☐ Warning ☐ Guidance ☐ Bad Dream ☐ Good Dream ☐ Prophetic Dream

What Was the Dominant Emotion(s)?

Positive Emotion

☐ Joy
☐ Inspiration
☐ Peace
☐ Happy
☐ Celebration
☐ Hope
☐ Blessed
☐ Grateful

Negative Emotion

☐ Crying
☐ Anxiety
☐ Panic
☐ Sad
☐ Confused
☐ Grieved
☐ Traumatise
☐ Worried

Emotion Scale Ratings

6 — Very Happy
5
4
3
2
1 — Not at a all

My Prophetic Dream Journal

Explain The Feeling

Possible Meaning of Dream

Prayer and Scripture Response

My Prophetic Dream Journal

Date, Time & Venue

Dream Title

Dream Description

_____
_____
_____
_____
_____
_____
_____
_____
_____

Type of Dream: ☐ Warning ☐ Guidance ☐ Bad Dream ☐ Good Dream ☐ Prophetic Dream

What Was the Dominant Emotion(s)?

Positive Emotion	Negative Emotion	Emotion Scale Ratings
☐ Joy	☐ Crying	☺ **6** — Very Happy
☐ Inspiration	☐ Anxiety	☺ **5**
☐ Peace	☐ Panic	☺ **4**
☐ Happy	☐ Sad	☹ **3**
☐ Celebration	☐ Confused	☹ **2**
☐ Hope	☐ Grieved	☹ **1** — Not at a all
☐ Blessed	☐ Traumatise	
☐ Grateful	☐ Worried	

My Prophetic Dream Journal

Explain The Feeling

Possible Meaning of Dream

Prayer and Scripture Response

My Prophetic Dream Journal

Date, Time & Venue

Dream Title

Dream Description

_____
_____
_____
_____
_____
_____
_____
_____
_____

Type of Dream: ☐ Warning ☐ Guidance ☐ Bad Dream ☐ Good Dream ☐ Prophetic Dream

What Was the Dominant Emotion(s)?

Positive Emotion
☐ Joy
☐ Inspiration
☐ Peace
☐ Happy
☐ Celebration
☐ Hope
☐ Blessed
☐ Grateful

Negative Emotion
☐ Crying
☐ Anxiety
☐ Panic
☐ Sad
☐ Confused
☐ Grieved
☐ Traumatise
☐ Worried

Emotion Scale Ratings
😄 6   Very Happy
🙂 5
😐 4
🙁 3
😟 2
😢 1   Not at a all

My Prophetic Dream Journal

Explain The Feeling

Possible Meaning of Dream

Prayer and Scripture Response

My Prophetic Dream Journal

Date, Time & Venue

Dream Title

Dream Description

_____
_____
_____
_____
_____
_____
_____
_____
_____
_____

Type of Dream: ☐ Warning ☐ Guidance ☐ Bad Dream ☐ Good Dream ☐ Prophetic Dream

What Was the Dominant Emotion(s)?

Positive Emotion	Negative Emotion	Emotion Scale Ratings
☐ Joy	☐ Crying	😃 6 Very Happy
☐ Inspiration	☐ Anxiety	🙂 5
☐ Peace	☐ Panic	😐 4
☐ Happy	☐ Sad	🙁 3
☐ Celebration	☐ Confused	😟 2
☐ Hope	☐ Grieved	
☐ Blessed	☐ Traumatise	😣 1 Not at a all
☐ Grateful	☐ Worried	

My Prophetic Dream Journal

Explain The Feeling

Possible Meaning of Dream

Prayer and Scripture Response

My Prophetic Dream Journal

Date, Time & Venue

Dream Title

Dream Description

_____
_____
_____
_____
_____
_____
_____
_____
_____
_____
_____

Type of Dream: ☐ Warning ☐ Guidance ☐ Bad Dream ☐ Good Dream ☐ Prophetic Dream

What Was the Dominant Emotion(s)?

Positive Emotion	Negative Emotion	Emotion Scale Ratings
☐ Joy	☐ Crying	😃 6 — Very Happy
☐ Inspiration	☐ Anxiety	🙂 5
☐ Peace	☐ Panic	😐 4
☐ Happy	☐ Sad	🙁 3
☐ Celebration	☐ Confused	
☐ Hope	☐ Grieved	😟 2
☐ Blessed	☐ Traumatise	
☐ Grateful	☐ Worried	😢 1 — Not at a all

My Prophetic Dream Journal

Explain The Feeling

Possible Meaning of Dream

Prayer and Scripture Response

My Prophetic Dream Journal

Date, Time & Venue

Dream Title

Dream Description

_____
_____
_____
_____
_____
_____
_____
_____
_____
_____

Type of Dream: ☐ Warning ☐ Guidance ☐ Bad Dream ☐ Good Dream ☐ Prophetic Dream

What Was the Dominant Emotion(s)?

Positive Emotion	Negative Emotion	Emotion Scale Ratings
☐ Joy	☐ Crying	😀 6 — Very Happy
☐ Inspiration	☐ Anxiety	🙂 5
☐ Peace	☐ Panic	😐 4
☐ Happy	☐ Sad	🙁 3
☐ Celebration	☐ Confused	
☐ Hope	☐ Grieved	😟 2
☐ Blessed	☐ Traumatise	
☐ Grateful	☐ Worried	😞 1 — Not at a all

My Prophetic Dream Journal

Explain The Feeling

Possible Meaning of Dream

Prayer and Scripture Response

My Prophetic Dream Journal

Date, Time & Venue

Dream Title

Dream Description

_____
_____
_____
_____
_____
_____
_____
_____
_____

Type of Dream: ☐ Warning ☐ Guidance ☐ Bad Dream ☐ Good Dream ☐ Prophetic Dream

What Was the Dominant Emotion(s)?

Positive Emotion
☐ Joy
☐ Inspiration
☐ Peace
☐ Happy
☐ Celebration
☐ Hope
☐ Blessed
☐ Grateful

Negative Emotion
☐ Crying
☐ Anxiety
☐ Panic
☐ Sad
☐ Confused
☐ Grieved
☐ Traumatise
☐ Worried

Emotion Scale Ratings
😀 6 — Very Happy
🙂 5
😐 4
🙁 3
😟 2
😣 1 — Not at a all

My Prophetic Dream Journal

Explain The Feeling

Possible Meaning of Dream

Prayer and Scripture Response

My Prophetic Dream Journal

Date, Time & Venue

Dream Title

Dream Description

_____
_____
_____
_____
_____
_____
_____
_____
_____

Type of Dream: ☐ Warning ☐ Guidance ☐ Bad Dream ☐ Good Dream ☐ Prophetic Dream

What Was the Dominant Emotion(s)?

Positive Emotion
☐ Joy
☐ Inspiration
☐ Peace
☐ Happy
☐ Celebration
☐ Hope
☐ Blessed
☐ Grateful

Negative Emotion
☐ Crying
☐ Anxiety
☐ Panic
☐ Sad
☐ Confused
☐ Grieved
☐ Traumatise
☐ Worried

Emotion Scale Ratings
😀 6 Very Happy
🙂 5
😐 4
🙁 3
😟 2
😣 1 Not at a all

My Prophetic Dream Journal

Explain The Feeling

Possible Meaning of Dream

Prayer and Scripture Response

My Prophetic Dream Journal

Date, Time & Venue

Dream Title

Dream Description

_____
_____
_____
_____
_____
_____
_____
_____
_____

Type of Dream: ☐ Warning ☐ Guidance ☐ Bad Dream ☐ Good Dream ☐ Prophetic Dream

What Was the Dominant Emotion(s)?

Positive Emotion
☐ Joy
☐ Inspiration
☐ Peace
☐ Happy
☐ Celebration
☐ Hope
☐ Blessed
☐ Grateful

Negative Emotion
☐ Crying
☐ Anxiety
☐ Panic
☐ Sad
☐ Confused
☐ Grieved
☐ Traumatise
☐ Worried

Emotion Scale Ratings
😃 6   Very Happy
🙂 5
😐 4
🙁 3
😟 2
😥 1   Not at a all

My Prophetic Dream Journal

Explain The Feeling

Possible Meaning of Dream

Prayer and Scripture Response

My Prophetic Dream Journal

Date, Time & Venue

Dream Title

Dream Description

Type of Dream: ☐ Warning ☐ Guidance ☐ Bad Dream ☐ Good Dream ☐ Prophetic Dream

What Was the Dominant Emotion(s)?

Positive Emotion	Negative Emotion	Emotion Scale Ratings
☐ Joy	☐ Crying	😀 6 Very Happy
☐ Inspiration	☐ Anxiety	🙂 5
☐ Peace	☐ Panic	😐 4
☐ Happy	☐ Sad	🙁 3
☐ Celebration	☐ Confused	
☐ Hope	☐ Grieved	😟 2
☐ Blessed	☐ Traumatise	😞 1 Not at a all
☐ Grateful	☐ Worried	

My Prophetic Dream Journal

Explain The Feeling

Possible Meaning of Dream

Prayer and Scripture Response

My Prophetic Dream Journal

Date, Time & Venue

Dream Title

Dream Description

_____
_____
_____
_____
_____
_____
_____
_____
_____
_____

Type of Dream: ☐ Warning ☐ Guidance ☐ Bad Dream ☐ Good Dream ☐ Prophetic Dream

What Was the Dominant Emotion(s)?

Positive Emotion

☐ Joy
☐ Inspiration
☐ Peace
☐ Happy
☐ Celebration
☐ Hope
☐ Blessed
☐ Grateful

Negative Emotion

☐ Crying
☐ Anxiety
☐ Panic
☐ Sad
☐ Confused
☐ Grieved
☐ Traumatise
☐ Worried

Emotion Scale Ratings

6 — Very Happy
5
4
3
2
1 — Not at a all

My Prophetic Dream Journal

Explain The Feeling

Possible Meaning of Dream

Prayer and Scripture Response

My Prophetic Dream Journal

Date, Time & Venue

Dream Title

Dream Description

_____
_____
_____
_____
_____
_____
_____
_____
_____
_____

Type of Dream: ☐ Warning ☐ Guidance ☐ Bad Dream ☐ Good Dream ☐ Prophetic Dream

What Was the Dominant Emotion(s)?

Positive Emotion	Negative Emotion	Emotion Scale Ratings
☐ Joy	☐ Crying	🙂 6 — Very Happy
☐ Inspiration	☐ Anxiety	🙂 5
☐ Peace	☐ Panic	😐 4
☐ Happy	☐ Sad	🙁 3
☐ Celebration	☐ Confused	😟 2
☐ Hope	☐ Grieved	
☐ Blessed	☐ Traumatise	😞 1 — Not at a all
☐ Grateful	☐ Worried	

My Prophetic Dream Journal

Explain The Feeling

Possible Meaning of Dream

Prayer and Scripture Response

My Prophetic Dream Journal

Date, Time & Venue

Dream Title

Dream Description

_____
_____
_____
_____
_____
_____
_____
_____
_____

Type of Dream: ☐ Warning ☐ Guidance ☐ Bad Dream ☐ Good Dream ☐ Prophetic Dream

What Was the Dominant Emotion(s)?

Positive Emotion

☐ Joy
☐ Inspiration
☐ Peace
☐ Happy
☐ Celebration
☐ Hope
☐ Blessed
☐ Grateful

Negative Emotion

☐ Crying
☐ Anxiety
☐ Panic
☐ Sad
☐ Confused
☐ Grieved
☐ Traumatise
☐ Worried

Emotion Scale Ratings

😀 6   Very Happy
🙂 5
😐 4
🙁 3
😟 2
😢 1   Not at a all

My Prophetic Dream Journal

Explain The Feeling

Possible Meaning of Dream

Prayer and Scripture Response

My Prophetic Dream Journal

Date, Time & Venue

Dream Title

Dream Description

_____
_____
_____
_____
_____
_____
_____
_____
_____

Type of Dream: ☐ Warning ☐ Guidance ☐ Bad Dream ☐ Good Dream ☐ Prophetic Dream

What Was the Dominant Emotion(s)?

Positive Emotion
☐ Joy
☐ Inspiration
☐ Peace
☐ Happy
☐ Celebration
☐ Hope
☐ Blessed
☐ Grateful

Negative Emotion
☐ Crying
☐ Anxiety
☐ Panic
☐ Sad
☐ Confused
☐ Grieved
☐ Traumatise
☐ Worried

Emotion Scale Ratings
😀 6   Very Happy
🙂 5
😐 4
🙁 3
😟 2
😢 1   Not at a all

My Prophetic Dream Journal

Explain The Feeling

Possible Meaning of Dream

Prayer and Scripture Response

My Prophetic Dream Journal

Date, Time & Venue

Dream Title

Dream Description

_____
_____
_____
_____
_____
_____
_____
_____
_____

Type of Dream: ☐ Warning ☐ Guidance ☐ Bad Dream ☐ Good Dream ☐ Prophetic Dream

What Was the Dominant Emotion(s)?

Positive Emotion	Negative Emotion	Emotion Scale Ratings
☐ Joy	☐ Crying	😃 6 Very Happy
☐ Inspiration	☐ Anxiety	🙂 5
☐ Peace	☐ Panic	😐 4
☐ Happy	☐ Sad	🙁 3
☐ Celebration	☐ Confused	
☐ Hope	☐ Grieved	😟 2
☐ Blessed	☐ Traumatise	
☐ Grateful	☐ Worried	😞 1 Not at a all

My Prophetic Dream Journal

Explain The Feeling

Possible Meaning of Dream

Prayer and Scripture Response

My Prophetic Dream Journal

Date, Time & Venue

Dream Title

Dream Description

_____

_____

_____

_____

_____

_____

_____

_____

_____

Type of Dream: ☐ Warning ☐ Guidance ☐ Bad Dream ☐ Good Dream ☐ Prophetic Dream

What Was the Dominant Emotion(s)?

Positive Emotion	Negative Emotion	Emotion Scale Ratings
☐ Joy	☐ Crying	🙂 6 Very Happy
☐ Inspiration	☐ Anxiety	🙂 5
☐ Peace	☐ Panic	😐 4
☐ Happy	☐ Sad	🙁 3
☐ Celebration	☐ Confused	
☐ Hope	☐ Grieved	🙁 2
☐ Blessed	☐ Traumatise	
☐ Grateful	☐ Worried	😢 1 Not at a all

My Prophetic Dream Journal

Explain The Feeling

Possible Meaning of Dream

Prayer and Scripture Response

My Prophetic Dream Journal

Date, Time & Venue

Dream Title

Dream Description

_____
_____
_____
_____
_____
_____
_____
_____
_____

Type of Dream: ☐ Warning ☐ Guidance ☐ Bad Dream ☐ Good Dream ☐ Prophetic Dream

What Was the Dominant Emotion(s)?

Positive Emotion

☐ Joy
☐ Inspiration
☐ Peace
☐ Happy
☐ Celebration
☐ Hope
☐ Blessed
☐ Grateful

Negative Emotion

☐ Crying
☐ Anxiety
☐ Panic
☐ Sad
☐ Confused
☐ Grieved
☐ Traumatise
☐ Worried

Emotion Scale Ratings

6 — Very Happy
5
4
3
2
1 — Not at a all

My Prophetic Dream Journal

Explain The Feeling

Possible Meaning of Dream

Prayer and Scripture Response

My Prophetic Dream Journal

Date, Time & Venue

Dream Title

Dream Description

_____
_____
_____
_____
_____
_____
_____
_____
_____

Type of Dream: ☐ Warning ☐ Guidance ☐ Bad Dream ☐ Good Dream ☐ Prophetic Dream

What Was the Dominant Emotion(s)?

Positive Emotion	Negative Emotion	Emotion Scale Ratings
☐ Joy	☐ Crying	😃 6 Very Happy
☐ Inspiration	☐ Anxiety	🙂 5
☐ Peace	☐ Panic	😐 4
☐ Happy	☐ Sad	🙁 3
☐ Celebration	☐ Confused	😟 2
☐ Hope	☐ Grieved	
☐ Blessed	☐ Traumatise	😢 1 Not at a all
☐ Grateful	☐ Worried	

My Prophetic Dream Journal

Explain The Feeling

Possible Meaning of Dream

Prayer and Scripture Response

My Prophetic Dream Journal

Date, Time & Venue

Dream Title

Dream Description

_____
_____
_____
_____
_____
_____
_____
_____
_____
_____

Type of Dream: ☐ Warning ☐ Guidance ☐ Bad Dream ☐ Good Dream ☐ Prophetic Dream

What Was the Dominant Emotion(s)?

Positive Emotion	Negative Emotion	Emotion Scale Ratings
☐ Joy	☐ Crying	😃 6 Very Happy
☐ Inspiration	☐ Anxiety	🙂 5
☐ Peace	☐ Panic	😐 4
☐ Happy	☐ Sad	🙁 3
☐ Celebration	☐ Confused	😟 2
☐ Hope	☐ Grieved	
☐ Blessed	☐ Traumatise	😞 1 Not at a all
☐ Grateful	☐ Worried	

My Prophetic Dream Journal

Explain The Feeling

Possible Meaning of Dream

Prayer and Scripture Response

My Prophetic Dream Journal

Date, Time & Venue

Dream Title

Dream Description

Type of Dream: ☐ Warning ☐ Guidance ☐ Bad Dream ☐ Good Dream ☐ Prophetic Dream

What Was the Dominant Emotion(s)?

Positive Emotion

☐ Joy
☐ Inspiration
☐ Peace
☐ Happy
☐ Celebration
☐ Hope
☐ Blessed
☐ Grateful

Negative Emotion

☐ Crying
☐ Anxiety
☐ Panic
☐ Sad
☐ Confused
☐ Grieved
☐ Traumatise
☐ Worried

Emotion Scale Ratings

🙂 6 Very Happy
🙂 5
😐 4
🙁 3
☹️ 2
😢 1 Not at a all

My Prophetic Dream Journal

Explain The Feeling

Possible Meaning of Dream

Prayer and Scripture Response

My Prophetic Dream Journal

Date, Time & Venue

Dream Title

Dream Description

_____
_____
_____
_____
_____
_____
_____
_____
_____
_____

Type of Dream: ☐ Warning ☐ Guidance ☐ Bad Dream ☐ Good Dream ☐ Prophetic Dream

What Was the Dominant Emotion(s)?

Positive Emotion	Negative Emotion	Emotion Scale Ratings
☐ Joy	☐ Crying	😃 6 Very Happy
☐ Inspiration	☐ Anxiety	🙂 5
☐ Peace	☐ Panic	😐 4
☐ Happy	☐ Sad	🙁 3
☐ Celebration	☐ Confused	☹️ 2
☐ Hope	☐ Grieved	😢 1 Not at a all
☐ Blessed	☐ Traumatise	
☐ Grateful	☐ Worried	

My Prophetic Dream Journal

Explain The Feeling

Possible Meaning of Dream

Prayer and Scripture Response

My Prophetic Dream Journal

Date, Time & Venue

Dream Title

Dream Description

_____
_____
_____
_____
_____
_____
_____
_____
_____
_____

Type of Dream: ☐ Warning ☐ Guidance ☐ Bad Dream ☐ Good Dream ☐ Prophetic Dream

What Was the Dominant Emotion(s)?

Positive Emotion	Negative Emotion	Emotion Scale Ratings
☐ Joy	☐ Crying	😀 6 Very Happy
☐ Inspiration	☐ Anxiety	🙂 5
☐ Peace	☐ Panic	😐 4
☐ Happy	☐ Sad	🙁 3
☐ Celebration	☐ Confused	😟 2
☐ Hope	☐ Grieved	
☐ Blessed	☐ Traumatise	😢 1 Not at a all
☐ Grateful	☐ Worried	

My Prophetic Dream Journal

Explain The Feeling

Possible Meaning of Dream

Prayer and Scripture Response

My Prophetic Dream Journal

Date, Time & Venue

Dream Title

Dream Description

_____
_____
_____
_____
_____
_____
_____
_____
_____

Type of Dream: ☐ Warning ☐ Guidance ☐ Bad Dream ☐ Good Dream ☐ Prophetic Dream

What Was the Dominant Emotion(s)?

Positive Emotion	Negative Emotion	Emotion Scale Ratings
☐ Joy	☐ Crying	😃 6 — Very Happy
☐ Inspiration	☐ Anxiety	🙂 5
☐ Peace	☐ Panic	😐 4
☐ Happy	☐ Sad	🙁 3
☐ Celebration	☐ Confused	😟 2
☐ Hope	☐ Grieved	
☐ Blessed	☐ Traumatise	😞 1 — Not at a all
☐ Grateful	☐ Worried	

My Prophetic Dream Journal

Explain The Feeling

Possible Meaning of Dream

Prayer and Scripture Response

My Prophetic Dream Journal

Date, Time & Venue

Dream Title

Dream Description

_____
_____
_____
_____
_____
_____
_____
_____
_____
_____

Type of Dream: ☐ Warning ☐ Guidance ☐ Bad Dream ☐ Good Dream ☐ Prophetic Dream

What Was the Dominant Emotion(s)?

Positive Emotion

☐ Joy
☐ Inspiration
☐ Peace
☐ Happy
☐ Celebration
☐ Hope
☐ Blessed
☐ Grateful

Negative Emotion

☐ Crying
☐ Anxiety
☐ Panic
☐ Sad
☐ Confused
☐ Grieved
☐ Traumatise
☐ Worried

Emotion Scale Ratings

🙂 6   Very Happy
🙂 5
😐 4
🙁 3
😟 2
😣 1   Not at a all

My Prophetic Dream Journal

Explain The Feeling

Possible Meaning of Dream

Prayer and Scripture Response

My Prophetic Dream Journal

Date, Time & Venue

Dream Title

Dream Description

_____
_____
_____
_____
_____
_____
_____
_____
_____

Type of Dream: ☐ Warning ☐ Guidance ☐ Bad Dream ☐ Good Dream ☐ Prophetic Dream

What Was the Dominant Emotion(s)?

Positive Emotion
☐ Joy
☐ Inspiration
☐ Peace
☐ Happy
☐ Celebration
☐ Hope
☐ Blessed
☐ Grateful

Negative Emotion
☐ Crying
☐ Anxiety
☐ Panic
☐ Sad
☐ Confused
☐ Grieved
☐ Traumatise
☐ Worried

Emotion Scale Ratings
😃 6 Very Happy
🙂 5
😐 4
🙁 3
😟 2
😣 1 Not at a all

My Prophetic Dream Journal

Explain The Feeling

Possible Meaning of Dream

Prayer and Scripture Response

My Prophetic Dream Journal

Date, Time & Venue

Dream Title

Dream Description

_____
_____
_____
_____
_____
_____
_____
_____
_____
_____

Type of Dream: ☐ Warning ☐ Guidance ☐ Bad Dream ☐ Good Dream ☐ Prophetic Dream

What Was the Dominant Emotion(s)?

Positive Emotion	Negative Emotion	Emotion Scale Ratings	
☐ Joy	☐ Crying	😄 6	Very Happy
☐ Inspiration	☐ Anxiety	🙂 5	
☐ Peace	☐ Panic	😐 4	
☐ Happy	☐ Sad	🙁 3	
☐ Celebration	☐ Confused	😟 2	
☐ Hope	☐ Grieved		
☐ Blessed	☐ Traumatise	😣 1	Not at a all
☐ Grateful	☐ Worried		

My Prophetic Dream Journal

Explain The Feeling

Possible Meaning of Dream

Prayer and Scripture Response

My Prophetic Dream Journal

— Date, Time & Venue —

— Dream Title —

Dream Description

_____
_____
_____
_____
_____
_____
_____
_____
_____
_____

Type of Dream: ☐ Warning ☐ Guidance ☐ Bad Dream ☐ Good Dream ☐ Prophetic Dream

What Was the Dominant Emotion(s)?

Positive Emotion
☐ Joy
☐ Inspiration
☐ Peace
☐ Happy
☐ Celebration
☐ Hope
☐ Blessed
☐ Grateful

Negative Emotion
☐ Crying
☐ Anxiety
☐ Panic
☐ Sad
☐ Confused
☐ Grieved
☐ Traumatise
☐ Worried

Emotion Scale Ratings
😀 6 — Very Happy
🙂 5
😐 4
🙁 3
😟 2
😫 1 — Not at a all

My Prophetic Dream Journal

Explain The Feeling

Possible Meaning of Dream

Prayer and Scripture Response

My Prophetic Dream Journal

Date, Time & Venue

Dream Title

Dream Description

_____
_____
_____
_____
_____
_____
_____
_____
_____

Type of Dream: ☐ Warning ☐ Guidance ☐ Bad Dream ☐ Good Dream ☐ Prophetic Dream

What Was the Dominant Emotion(s)?

Positive Emotion	Negative Emotion	Emotion Scale Ratings
☐ Joy	☐ Crying	😃 6 Very Happy
☐ Inspiration	☐ Anxiety	🙂 5
☐ Peace	☐ Panic	😐 4
☐ Happy	☐ Sad	🙁 3
☐ Celebration	☐ Confused	😟 2
☐ Hope	☐ Grieved	
☐ Blessed	☐ Traumatise	😢 1 Not at a all
☐ Grateful	☐ Worried	

My Prophetic Dream Journal

Explain The Feeling

Possible Meaning of Dream

Prayer and Scripture Response

My Prophetic Dream Journal

Date, Time & Venue

Dream Title

Dream Description

Type of Dream: ☐ Warning ☐ Guidance ☐ Bad Dream ☐ Good Dream ☐ Prophetic Dream

What Was the Dominant Emotion(s)?

Positive Emotion	Negative Emotion	Emotion Scale Ratings
☐ Joy	☐ Crying	😀 6 Very Happy
☐ Inspiration	☐ Anxiety	🙂 5
☐ Peace	☐ Panic	😐 4
☐ Happy	☐ Sad	🙁 3
☐ Celebration	☐ Confused	
☐ Hope	☐ Grieved	😟 2
☐ Blessed	☐ Traumatise	
☐ Grateful	☐ Worried	😢 1 Not at a all

My Prophetic Dream Journal

Explain The Feeling

Possible Meaning of Dream

Prayer and Scripture Response

My Prophetic Dream Journal

Date, Time & Venue

Dream Title

Dream Description

_____
_____
_____
_____
_____
_____
_____
_____
_____
_____

Type of Dream: ☐ Warning ☐ Guidance ☐ Bad Dream ☐ Good Dream ☐ Prophetic Dream

What Was the Dominant Emotion(s)?

Positive Emotion	Negative Emotion	Emotion Scale Ratings
☐ Joy	☐ Crying	😀 6 Very Happy
☐ Inspiration	☐ Anxiety	🙂 5
☐ Peace	☐ Panic	😐 4
☐ Happy	☐ Sad	🙁 3
☐ Celebration	☐ Confused	😟 2
☐ Hope	☐ Grieved	😢 1 Not at a all
☐ Blessed	☐ Traumatise	
☐ Grateful	☐ Worried	

My Prophetic Dream Journal

Explain The Feeling

Possible Meaning of Dream

Prayer and Scripture Response

My Prophetic Dream Journal

Date, Time & Venue

Dream Title

Dream Description

_____
_____
_____
_____
_____
_____
_____
_____
_____
_____

Type of Dream: ☐ Warning ☐ Guidance ☐ Bad Dream ☐ Good Dream ☐ Prophetic Dream

What Was the Dominant Emotion(s)?

Positive Emotion
☐ Joy
☐ Inspiration
☐ Peace
☐ Happy
☐ Celebration
☐ Hope
☐ Blessed
☐ Grateful

Negative Emotion
☐ Crying
☐ Anxiety
☐ Panic
☐ Sad
☐ Confused
☐ Grieved
☐ Traumatise
☐ Worried

Emotion Scale Ratings
😃 6   Very Happy
🙂 5
😐 4
🙁 3
😟 2
😢 1   Not at a all

My Prophetic Dream Journal

Explain The Feeling

Possible Meaning of Dream

Prayer and Scripture Response

My Prophetic Dream Journal

Date, Time & Venue

Dream Title

Dream Description

_____
_____
_____
_____
_____
_____
_____
_____
_____
_____

Type of Dream: ☐ Warning ☐ Guidance ☐ Bad Dream ☐ Good Dream ☐ Prophetic Dream

What Was the Dominant Emotion(s)?

Positive Emotion
☐ Joy
☐ Inspiration
☐ Peace
☐ Happy
☐ Celebration
☐ Hope
☐ Blessed
☐ Grateful

Negative Emotion
☐ Crying
☐ Anxiety
☐ Panic
☐ Sad
☐ Confused
☐ Grieved
☐ Traumatise
☐ Worried

Emotion Scale Ratings
😃 6 — Very Happy
🙂 5
😐 4
🙁 3
😟 2
😢 1 — Not at a all

My Prophetic Dream Journal

Explain The Feeling

Possible Meaning of Dream

Prayer and Scripture Response

My Prophetic Dream Journal

Date, Time & Venue

Dream Title

Dream Description

_____

_____

_____

_____

_____

_____

_____

_____

_____

Type of Dream: ☐ Warning ☐ Guidance ☐ Bad Dream ☐ Good Dream ☐ Prophetic Dream

What Was the Dominant Emotion(s)?

Positive Emotion

☐ Joy
☐ Inspiration
☐ Peace
☐ Happy
☐ Celebration
☐ Hope
☐ Blessed
☐ Grateful

Negative Emotion

☐ Crying
☐ Anxiety
☐ Panic
☐ Sad
☐ Confused
☐ Grieved
☐ Traumatise
☐ Worried

Emotion Scale Ratings

6 — Very Happy
5
4
3
2
1 — Not at a all

My Prophetic Dream Journal

Explain The Feeling

Possible Meaning of Dream

Prayer and Scripture Response

My Prophetic Dream Journal

Date, Time & Venue

Dream Title

Dream Description

Type of Dream: ☐ Warning ☐ Guidance ☐ Bad Dream ☐ Good Dream ☐ Prophetic Dream

What Was the Dominant Emotion(s)?

Positive Emotion

☐ Joy
☐ Inspiration
☐ Peace
☐ Happy
☐ Celebration
☐ Hope
☐ Blessed
☐ Grateful

Negative Emotion

☐ Crying
☐ Anxiety
☐ Panic
☐ Sad
☐ Confused
☐ Grieved
☐ Traumatise
☐ Worried

Emotion Scale Ratings

😀 6   Very Happy
🙂 5
😐 4
🙁 3
😟 2
😢 1   Not at a all

My Prophetic Dream Journal

Explain The Feeling

Possible Meaning of Dream

Prayer and Scripture Response

My Prophetic Dream Journal

Date, Time & Venue

Dream Title

Dream Description

_____

_____

_____

_____

_____

_____

_____

_____

_____

Type of Dream: ☐ Warning ☐ Guidance ☐ Bad Dream ☐ Good Dream ☐ Prophetic Dream

What Was the Dominant Emotion(s)?

Positive Emotion
☐ Joy
☐ Inspiration
☐ Peace
☐ Happy
☐ Celebration
☐ Hope
☐ Blessed
☐ Grateful

Negative Emotion
☐ Crying
☐ Anxiety
☐ Panic
☐ Sad
☐ Confused
☐ Grieved
☐ Traumatise
☐ Worried

Emotion Scale Ratings
😃 **6** Very Happy
🙂 **5**
😐 **4**
🙁 **3**
😟 **2**
😣 **1** Not at a all

My Prophetic Dream Journal

Explain The Feeling

Possible Meaning of Dream

Prayer and Scripture Response

My Prophetic Dream Journal

Date, Time & Venue

Dream Title

Dream Description

_____
_____
_____
_____
_____
_____
_____
_____
_____

Type of Dream: ☐ Warning ☐ Guidance ☐ Bad Dream ☐ Good Dream ☐ Prophetic Dream

What Was the Dominant Emotion(s)?

Positive Emotion	Negative Emotion	Emotion Scale Ratings
☐ Joy	☐ Crying	😃 6 Very Happy
☐ Inspiration	☐ Anxiety	🙂 5
☐ Peace	☐ Panic	😐 4
☐ Happy	☐ Sad	
☐ Celebration	☐ Confused	🙁 3
☐ Hope	☐ Grieved	2
☐ Blessed	☐ Traumatise	
☐ Grateful	☐ Worried	😢 1 Not at a all

My Prophetic Dream Journal

Explain The Feeling

Possible Meaning of Dream

Prayer and Scripture Response

My Prophetic Dream Journal

— Date, Time & Venue —

— Dream Title —

Dream Description

Type of Dream: ☐ Warning ☐ Guidance ☐ Bad Dream ☐ Good Dream ☐ Prophetic Dream

What Was the Dominant Emotion(s)?

Positive Emotion	Negative Emotion	Emotion Scale Ratings
☐ Joy	☐ Crying	😀 6 Very Happy
☐ Inspiration	☐ Anxiety	🙂 5
☐ Peace	☐ Panic	😐 4
☐ Happy	☐ Sad	🙁 3
☐ Celebration	☐ Confused	😟 2
☐ Hope	☐ Grieved	
☐ Blessed	☐ Traumatise	😢 1 Not at a all
☐ Grateful	☐ Worried	

My Prophetic Dream Journal

Explain The Feeling

Possible Meaning of Dream

Prayer and Scripture Response

My Prophetic Dream Journal

Date, Time & Venue

Dream Title

Dream Description

_____
_____
_____
_____
_____
_____
_____
_____
_____
_____

Type of Dream: ☐ Warning ☐ Guidance ☐ Bad Dream ☐ Good Dream ☐ Prophetic Dream

What Was the Dominant Emotion(s)?

Positive Emotion	Negative Emotion	Emotion Scale Ratings
☐ Joy	☐ Crying	😀 6 Very Happy
☐ Inspiration	☐ Anxiety	🙂 5
☐ Peace	☐ Panic	😐 4
☐ Happy	☐ Sad	🙁 3
☐ Celebration	☐ Confused	😟 2
☐ Hope	☐ Grieved	
☐ Blessed	☐ Traumatise	😢 1 Not at a all
☐ Grateful	☐ Worried	

My Prophetic Dream Journal

Explain The Feeling

Possible Meaning of Dream

Prayer and Scripture Response

My Prophetic Dream Journal

Date, Time & Venue

Dream Title

Dream Description

_____
_____
_____
_____
_____
_____
_____
_____
_____
_____

Type of Dream: ☐ Warning ☐ Guidance ☐ Bad Dream ☐ Good Dream ☐ Prophetic Dream

What Was the Dominant Emotion(s)?

Positive Emotion

☐ Joy
☐ Inspiration
☐ Peace
☐ Happy
☐ Celebration
☐ Hope
☐ Blessed
☐ Grateful

Negative Emotion

☐ Crying
☐ Anxiety
☐ Panic
☐ Sad
☐ Confused
☐ Grieved
☐ Traumatise
☐ Worried

Emotion Scale Ratings

6 — Very Happy
5
4
3
2
1 — Not at a all

My Prophetic Dream Journal

Explain The Feeling

Possible Meaning of Dream

Prayer and Scripture Response

My Prophetic Dream Journal

Date, Time & Venue

Dream Title

Dream Description

_____
_____
_____
_____
_____
_____
_____
_____
_____
_____

Type of Dream: ☐ Warning ☐ Guidance ☐ Bad Dream ☐ Good Dream ☐ Prophetic Dream

What Was the Dominant Emotion(s)?

Positive Emotion

☐ Joy
☐ Inspiration
☐ Peace
☐ Happy
☐ Celebration
☐ Hope
☐ Blessed
☐ Grateful

Negative Emotion

☐ Crying
☐ Anxiety
☐ Panic
☐ Sad
☐ Confused
☐ Grieved
☐ Traumatise
☐ Worried

Emotion Scale Ratings

🙂 6   Very Happy
🙂 5
😐 4
🙁 3
😟 2
😣 1   Not at a all

My Prophetic Dream Journal

Explain The Feeling

Possible Meaning of Dream

Prayer and Scripture Response

My Prophetic Dream Journal

Date, Time & Venue

Dream Title

Dream Description

_____
_____
_____
_____
_____
_____
_____
_____
_____
_____

Type of Dream: ☐ Warning ☐ Guidance ☐ Bad Dream ☐ Good Dream ☐ Prophetic Dream

What Was the Dominant Emotion(s)?

Positive Emotion	Negative Emotion	Emotion Scale Ratings
☐ Joy	☐ Crying	😃 6 Very Happy
☐ Inspiration	☐ Anxiety	🙂 5
☐ Peace	☐ Panic	😐 4
☐ Happy	☐ Sad	🙁 3
☐ Celebration	☐ Confused	😟 2
☐ Hope	☐ Grieved	
☐ Blessed	☐ Traumatise	😣 1 Not at a all
☐ Grateful	☐ Worried	

My Prophetic Dream Journal

Explain The Feeling

Possible Meaning of Dream

Prayer and Scripture Response

My Prophetic Dream Journal

Date, Time & Venue

Dream Title

Dream Description

_____
_____
_____
_____
_____
_____
_____
_____
_____

Type of Dream: ☐ Warning ☐ Guidance ☐ Bad Dream ☐ Good Dream ☐ Prophetic Dream

What Was the Dominant Emotion(s)?

Positive Emotion
☐ Joy
☐ Inspiration
☐ Peace
☐ Happy
☐ Celebration
☐ Hope
☐ Blessed
☐ Grateful

Negative Emotion
☐ Crying
☐ Anxiety
☐ Panic
☐ Sad
☐ Confused
☐ Grieved
☐ Traumatise
☐ Worried

Emotion Scale Ratings
6   Very Happy
5
4
3
2
1   Not at a all

My Prophetic Dream Journal

Explain The Feeling

Possible Meaning of Dream

Prayer and Scripture Response

My Prophetic Dream Journal

Date, Time & Venue

Dream Title

Dream Description

_____
_____
_____
_____
_____
_____
_____
_____
_____
_____

Type of Dream: ☐ Warning ☐ Guidance ☐ Bad Dream ☐ Good Dream ☐ Prophetic Dream

What Was the Dominant Emotion(s)?

Positive Emotion

☐ Joy
☐ Inspiration
☐ Peace
☐ Happy
☐ Celebration
☐ Hope
☐ Blessed
☐ Grateful

Negative Emotion

☐ Crying
☐ Anxiety
☐ Panic
☐ Sad
☐ Confused
☐ Grieved
☐ Traumatise
☐ Worried

Emotion Scale Ratings

6 Very Happy
5
4
3
2
1 Not at a all

My Prophetic Dream Journal

Explain The Feeling

Possible Meaning of Dream

Prayer and Scripture Response

My Prophetic Dream Journal

Date, Time & Venue

Dream Title

Dream Description

_____
_____
_____
_____
_____
_____
_____
_____
_____

Type of Dream: ☐ Warning ☐ Guidance ☐ Bad Dream ☐ Good Dream ☐ Prophetic Dream

What Was the Dominant Emotion(s)?

Positive Emotion	Negative Emotion	Emotion Scale Ratings	
☐ Joy	☐ Crying	😃 6	Very Happy
☐ Inspiration	☐ Anxiety	🙂 5	
☐ Peace	☐ Panic	😐 4	
☐ Happy	☐ Sad	🙁 3	
☐ Celebration	☐ Confused	😟 2	
☐ Hope	☐ Grieved	😩 1	Not at a all
☐ Blessed	☐ Traumatise		
☐ Grateful	☐ Worried		

My Prophetic Dream Journal

Explain The Feeling

Possible Meaning of Dream

Prayer and Scripture Response

My Prophetic Dream Journal

Date, Time & Venue

Dream Title

Dream Description

Type of Dream: ☐ Warning ☐ Guidance ☐ Bad Dream ☐ Good Dream ☐ Prophetic Dream

What Was the Dominant Emotion(s)?

Positive Emotion	Negative Emotion	Emotion Scale Ratings
☐ Joy	☐ Crying	😀 6 Very Happy
☐ Inspiration	☐ Anxiety	🙂 5
☐ Peace	☐ Panic	😐 4
☐ Happy	☐ Sad	🙁 3
☐ Celebration	☐ Confused	😟 2
☐ Hope	☐ Grieved	
☐ Blessed	☐ Traumatise	😢 1 Not at a all
☐ Grateful	☐ Worried	

My Prophetic Dream Journal

Explain The Feeling

Possible Meaning of Dream

Prayer and Scripture Response

My Prophetic Dream Journal

Date, Time & Venue

Dream Title

Dream Description

_____
_____
_____
_____
_____
_____
_____
_____
_____

Type of Dream: ☐ Warning ☐ Guidance ☐ Bad Dream ☐ Good Dream ☐ Prophetic Dream

What Was the Dominant Emotion(s)?

Positive Emotion	Negative Emotion	Emotion Scale Ratings
☐ Joy	☐ Crying	😄 6 Very Happy
☐ Inspiration	☐ Anxiety	🙂 5
☐ Peace	☐ Panic	😐 4
☐ Happy	☐ Sad	🙁 3
☐ Celebration	☐ Confused	😟 2
☐ Hope	☐ Grieved	
☐ Blessed	☐ Traumatise	😢 1 Not at a all
☐ Grateful	☐ Worried	

My Prophetic Dream Journal

Explain The Feeling

Possible Meaning of Dream

Prayer and Scripture Response

My Prophetic Dream Journal

Date, Time & Venue

Dream Title

Dream Description

_____
_____
_____
_____
_____
_____
_____
_____
_____

Type of Dream: ☐ Warning ☐ Guidance ☐ Bad Dream ☐ Good Dream ☐ Prophetic Dream

What Was the Dominant Emotion(s)?

Positive Emotion	Negative Emotion	Emotion Scale Ratings
☐ Joy	☐ Crying	😃 6 Very Happy
☐ Inspiration	☐ Anxiety	🙂 5
☐ Peace	☐ Panic	😐 4
☐ Happy	☐ Sad	
☐ Celebration	☐ Confused	🙁 3
☐ Hope	☐ Grieved	😟 2
☐ Blessed	☐ Traumatise	
☐ Grateful	☐ Worried	😣 1 Not at a all

My Prophetic Dream Journal

Explain The Feeling

Possible Meaning of Dream

Prayer and Scripture Response

My Prophetic Dream Journal

Date, Time & Venue

Dream Title

Dream Description

_____
_____
_____
_____
_____
_____
_____
_____
_____

Type of Dream: ☐ Warning ☐ Guidance ☐ Bad Dream ☐ Good Dream ☐ Prophetic Dream

What Was the Dominant Emotion(s)?

Positive Emotion	Negative Emotion	Emotion Scale Ratings
☐ Joy	☐ Crying	😃 6 — Very Happy
☐ Inspiration	☐ Anxiety	🙂 5
☐ Peace	☐ Panic	😐 4
☐ Happy	☐ Sad	🙁 3
☐ Celebration	☐ Confused	☹️ 2
☐ Hope	☐ Grieved	
☐ Blessed	☐ Traumatise	😢 1 — Not at a all
☐ Grateful	☐ Worried	

My Prophetic Dream Journal

Explain The Feeling

Possible Meaning of Dream

Prayer and Scripture Response

My Prophetic Dream Journal

Date, Time & Venue

Dream Title

Dream Description

_____
_____
_____
_____
_____
_____
_____
_____
_____
_____

Type of Dream: ☐ Warning ☐ Guidance ☐ Bad Dream ☐ Good Dream ☐ Prophetic Dream

What Was the Dominant Emotion(s)?

Positive Emotion

☐ Joy
☐ Inspiration
☐ Peace
☐ Happy
☐ Celebration
☐ Hope
☐ Blessed
☐ Grateful

Negative Emotion

☐ Crying
☐ Anxiety
☐ Panic
☐ Sad
☐ Confused
☐ Grieved
☐ Traumatise
☐ Worried

Emotion Scale Ratings

6 — Very Happy
5
4
3
2
1 — Not at a all

My Prophetic Dream Journal

Explain The Feeling

Possible Meaning of Dream

Prayer and Scripture Response

My Prophetic Dream Journal

── Date, Time & Venue ──

── Dream Title ──

Dream Description

_____

_____

_____

_____

_____

_____

_____

_____

_____

Type of Dream: ☐ Warning ☐ Guidance ☐ Bad Dream ☐ Good Dream ☐ Prophetic Dream

What Was the Dominant Emotion(s)?

Positive Emotion

☐ Joy
☐ Inspiration
☐ Peace
☐ Happy
☐ Celebration
☐ Hope
☐ Blessed
☐ Grateful

Negative Emotion

☐ Crying
☐ Anxiety
☐ Panic
☐ Sad
☐ Confused
☐ Grieved
☐ Traumatise
☐ Worried

Emotion Scale Ratings

6 — Very Happy
5
4
3
2
1 — Not at a all

My Prophetic Dream Journal

Explain The Feeling

Possible Meaning of Dream

Prayer and Scripture Response

My Prophetic Dream Journal

Date, Time & Venue

Dream Title

Dream Description

_____
_____
_____
_____
_____
_____
_____
_____
_____

Type of Dream: ☐ Warning ☐ Guidance ☐ Bad Dream ☐ Good Dream ☐ Prophetic Dream

What Was the Dominant Emotion(s)?

Positive Emotion

☐ Joy
☐ Inspiration
☐ Peace
☐ Happy
☐ Celebration
☐ Hope
☐ Blessed
☐ Grateful

Negative Emotion

☐ Crying
☐ Anxiety
☐ Panic
☐ Sad
☐ Confused
☐ Grieved
☐ Traumatise
☐ Worried

Emotion Scale Ratings

😀	6	Very Happy
🙂	5	
😐	4	
🙁	3	
😟	2	
😢	1	Not at a all

My Prophetic Dream Journal

Explain The Feeling

Possible Meaning of Dream

Prayer and Scripture Response

Made in United States
Orlando, FL
20 July 2022

19975026R00070